D1360918

BEN UNLEASHED

BEN UNLEASHED

by John Troy

Published by WILLOW CREEK PRESS
P.O. Box 300, Wautoma, WI 54982

Published July 1988

ISBN 0-932558-46-1

CONTENTS

SPRING

"Who ordered all this stuff from the fishing catalog?"

" . . . and opening day at that. How's Ben taking it?"

"No, a fishing license . . . A fishing license!"

"Flying squirrels nothing, it's Ben!"

"Can't you wait until I reel it in a little?"

"Yup, lots of snakes around, that's why I wear these snake boots.
Snakes can't bite that high."

"Thanks for oiling my reel Ben. I think."

"Hon, did you see my casting rod around?"

"I think I see your boomerang coming back, Ben."

"Don't even __think__ the word 'fix' around Ben!"

"Baking potatoes in tail pipes is a no-no, Ben."

"My, my, Ben, look what our neighbor has brought you for Father's Day."

"Boy I'm hungry! What I wouldn't give for a burger and a can of pop."

13

"Museum was broken into last night, Ben. Know anything about it?"

"Hey, what happened to my worms?!"

14

"Come on down, Ben, and I'll tighten that spring a little."

"Ben, go find a safe place and <u>sit</u>."

"This must be a first — a dog dish mugging!"

"A *cattle prod*?! No fair."

"So don't jump up and down every time I catch a fish."

"Ben was tying a tail on the kite and _what_ happened?"

"Is this your idea of a bird's eye view?"

"Let's go see how Ben is celebrating Easter."

"I don't know, rehearsing Swan Lake, maybe?"

*"Why do they always show
us dogs drooling . . .*

*. . . with our tongues
hanging down to
the ground . . .*

*. . . like we don't
have any manners."*

"We're not savages,
y'know!"

"Okay, I'm an animal.
So sue me."

"I can't wait to use this ultra-light, so let me know when you see a fish, Ben."

"Can't get used to those next-to-the-boat muskie strikes, can you?"

"On second thought, Ben, I'll just have them sunnyside."

"Sure you don't need a net, Ben?"

"Ever hear of a _net_?"

"Ben helped me land a muskie — should've used the net."

"How do you get your dog to go fishing with you?"   *"How do you get yours to stay home?"*

"I won't even ask."

"I hate it when he wings the frisbee!"

"So _that's_ how you've been winning those bass derbies!"

"... there's a good spot, there's another one, how about that one, nice drop off there ... "

"Wow, a honey tree — run home and get some jars, Ben, and _hurry!_"

"What do they call those salamanders? Water dogs, mud puppies . . ."

"Can't you seek your fortune somewhere else?!"

"No, no, don't hold on with your _teeth_!"

"Control yourself, Ben, plastic worms can't feel pain."

"So who packed this lunch?"

"I wish he could retrieve ducks that fast."

"I don't care if it is Independence Day — net my fish!"

"Give it up, Ben!"

"It helps him through the dog days."

"Ben's idea of catch-and-release is to catch the fish and release the bones."

"No, it's _not_ undersize, and no you're _not_ throwing it back!"

"I told you to bring the long handle net!"

"It says here ants can carry ten times their body weight, Ben . . . Ben?"

"What do you say we try the other side of the lake for awhile?"

"I'm trying to fish!"

"So what do you miss most on this trip, Ben? Fresh meat? Nice shower? . . ."

"Of course there's no hooks on your plug — do you think I'm dumb?"

"I distinctly said <u>salmon eggs!</u>"

"How come I don't hear you complaining about the heat?"

"Okay, okay, I'll take you hunting."

"What happened to my salmon net?!"

"Does the word 'shakedown' ring a bell!?"

"No Ben, a cupful, a cupful!"

"No, I haven't seen Ben. Have you seen Ben?"

"It's a protest alright, he doesn't want to go to the vet."

" . . . and then, before Tarzan could turn, the leopard, with a blood curdling scream . . ."

"Wow, Ben, look at the size of that swamp rabbit!"

"Gesundheit!"

"Bad place for a point."

"It's __not__ a job for Rin-Tin-Tin!"

"Ben gives a whole new meaning to the word 'retriever'."

"Sure, Ben — You're the
greatest rabbit dog that ever lived."

"Did your shooting improve today, Dear?"

"So, is your kabob hot enough?"

"It's Ben's idea — he's allergic to long swims in cold water."

"This is a heck of a way to start the duck season."

"See if I take you hunting again!"

"That's Ben's idea of hunting — search, find, and destroy."

"No Ben, nowadays it's apprehension and arrest, not 'off with his head'!"

"He was born to the sea."

"It takes Ben awhile to get into the swing of things."

"I like to believe Ben's life revolves around hunting. Then there are times . . . "

"Ben, I've seen you bowl, flycast, and shoot a gun — that's why."

"What are you supposed to be, my backup?"

"Today we hunt with a camera, Ben — how does that grab you?"

"Better loosen your string a little, Ben."

"Wow, a new record for Ben — a three second point."

"You're looking at Ben's best point of the day."

"Another miss! It's almost like there's no shot in these shells!"

"Oh well, I guess Ben doesn't want to go hunting, too bad . . . "

"I missed every duck last week — he hasn't talked to me since."

"Can't say this high grass really bothers Ben."

"First time your pup ever run jacks?"

"Okay, that settles it, we're having ham for Thanksgiving!"

"Looks to me like best two out of three falls."

"Cornering the steel shot market?"

"Hold on, Ben, <u>bark</u> is for squirrel, point is for <u>birds</u>."

"No, no, Ben! Cats don't retrieve ducks!"

"I know the feeling, Ben."

"I liked the old days when I'd pull you in the boat by the scruff of your neck!"

"No dog backs up a point tighter'n ol' Ben."

"I got a double on pheasants. This may take a while."

"Ben's idea of a successful hunt is not to come home hungry."

"Ben, you in there? Ben . . . ?"

"Ben, stop spritzing that buck lure on me!"

"We might just as well eat, Ben, there's not a duck in sight."

"He thinks if it works on snakes, why not rabbits."

"Okay, okay, I promise to take you deer hunting next time."

"Me? Hunt deer with a dog? Are you kidding?"

"C'mon, how could little Ben have dragged your deer off?"

"Oh yeah, can you <u>prove</u> Ben was chasing your bull!"

"Now *that's* what I call a nice snappy retrieve."

" . . . and this is how the camera got broken."

"First day of winter, get ready for a house guest."

"I think Goldie has had enough fishing for today, Ben."

"I don't mind you playing Tarzan, but if I hear 'where Jane' one more time . . . !"

"Do I see a hostage situation developing, Ben?"

"Where could he have gotten a reindeer on Christmas Day? . . . oh, no!"

"Guess what, Ben just tied a size 28 Royal Coachman!"

"So tell me, Ben, who spiked your water dish?"

"Talk about your heat-seeking missiles!"

"Dear, I thought you ordered cheese on the pizza?"

"I think he's onto our medicine-in-the-meatball trick."

"Don't try to outstare a cat if you want to use your eyes the rest of the day."

"Ben was doing Kung Fu and can't get his toes unhooked."

"What's that on the stairs, a snake?"

"This weather sure makes Ben peppy — especially when he's inside."

"So that's where you've been all day!"

"Ben read that you are what you eat — he think's he's turning into a horse."

"I take it you find your menu boring."

"Everybody has their own idea of heaven."

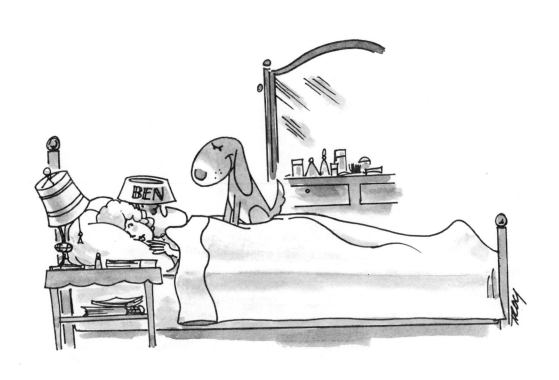

"Uh-oh, guess who we forgot to feed?"

"I knew I'd get it right
if I kept working on it."

"And who is *this* from?"

"I think Ben is losing the staring contest — it's getting near lunchtime."